It's Easy To Play
CABARET SONGS

Published by
Wise Publications
14-15 Berners Street, London W1T 3LJ, UK.

Exclusive Distributors:
Music Sales Limited
Distribution Centre, Newmarket Road, Bury St Edmunds,
Suffolk IP33 3YB, UK.
Music Sales Pty Limited
120 Rothschild Avenue, Rosebery, NSW 2018, Australia.

Order No. AM991144
ISBN: 978-1-84772-187-7
This book © Copyright 2007 Wise Publications,
a division of Music Sales Limited.

Edited by Jessica Williams.
Compiled by Nick Crispin.
Arranged and engraved by Camden Music.
Cover illustration by Liz Barrand.

Printed in the EU.

Your Guarantee of Quality
As publishers, we strive to produce every book
to the highest commercial standards.
The music has been freshly engraved and the book has
been carefully designed to minimise awkward page turns
and to make playing from it a real pleasure.
Particular care has been given to specifying acid-free,
neutral-sized paper made from pulps which have not been
elemental chlorine bleached. This pulp is from farmed
sustainable forests and was produced with special regard
for the environment.
Throughout, the printing and binding have been planned
to ensure a sturdy, attractive publication which should
give years of enjoyment.
If your copy fails to meet our high standards,
please inform us and we will gladly replace it.

www.musicsales.com

This publication is not authorised for sale in
the United States of America and / or Canada

Wise Publications
part of The Music Sales Group

London / New York / Paris / Sydney / Copenhagen / Berlin / Madrid / Tokyo

CABARET

Words by Fred Ebb
Music by John Kander

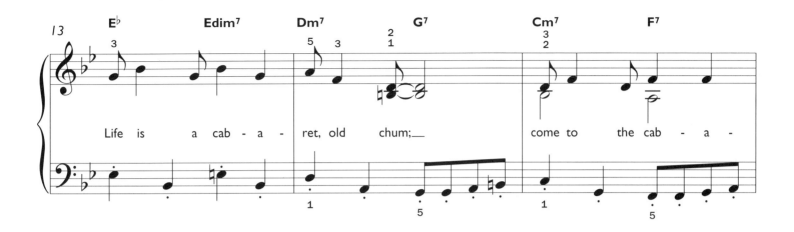

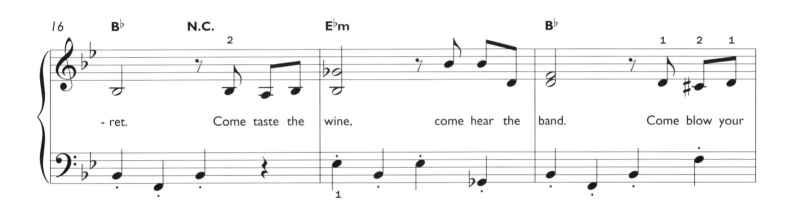

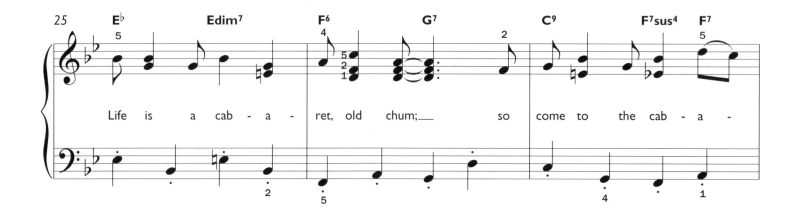

Life is a cab - a - ret, old chum;___ so come to the cab - a -

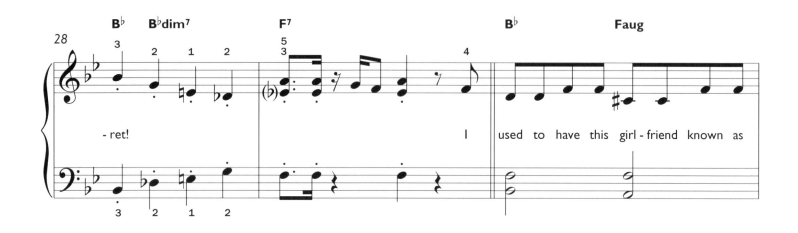

- ret!   I used to have this girl - friend known as

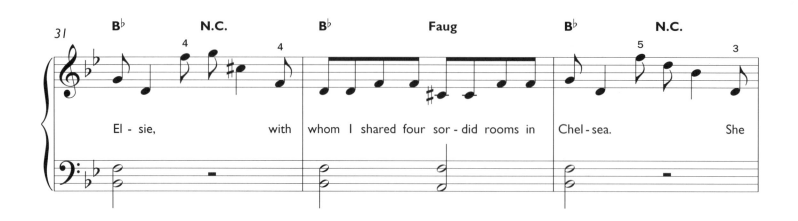

El - sie,   with whom I shared four sor - did rooms in Chel - sea.   She

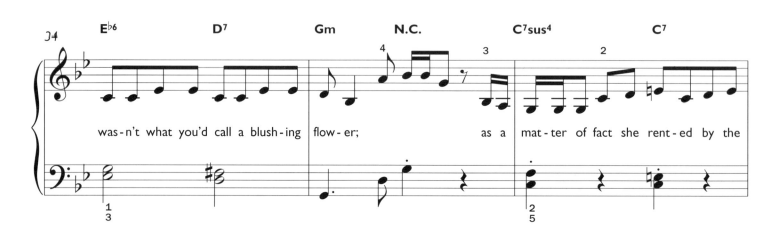

was - n't what you'd call a blush - ing flow - er;   as a mat - ter of fact she rent - ed by the

Rubato

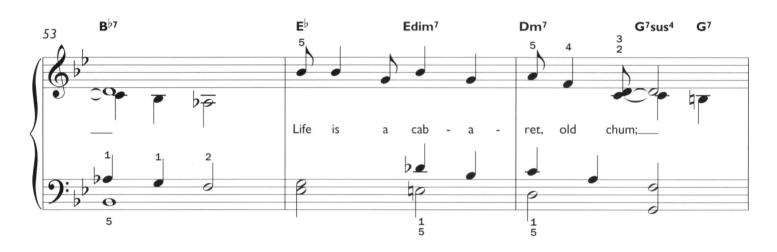

Slowly, with movement   **accel.**   **A tempo**

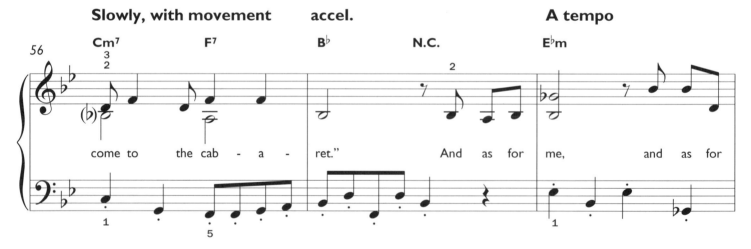

ad lib.

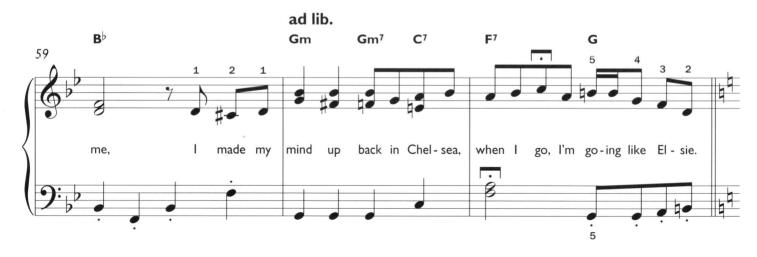

Slowly, accel. poco a poco

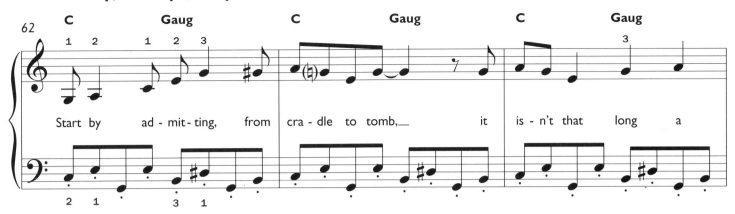

Start by ad - mit - ting, from cra - dle to tomb,___ it is - n't that long a

A tempo

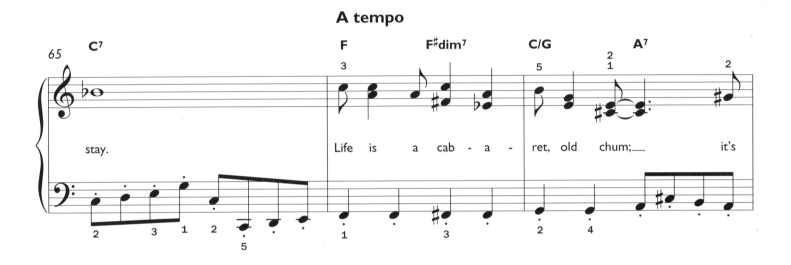

stay. Life is a cab - a - ret, old chum;___ it's

on - ly a___ cab - a - ret, old chum;___ and I love a

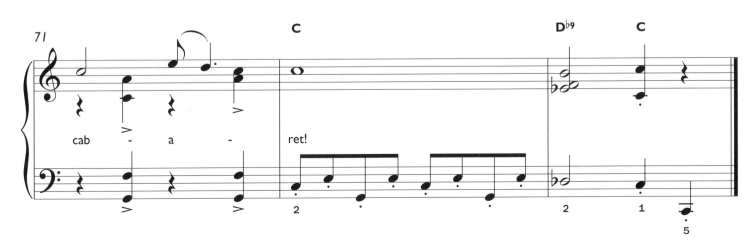

cab - a - ret!

7

BIG SPENDER

Words by Dorothy Fields
Music by Cy Coleman

to Coda ⊕

9

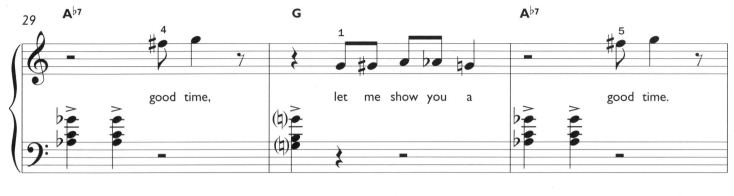

D.S. al Coda   ⊕ *Coda*

FALLING IN LOVE AGAIN

Words by Sammy Lerner & Friedrich Hollaender
Music by Friedrich Hollaender

With a lilt ♩ = 104

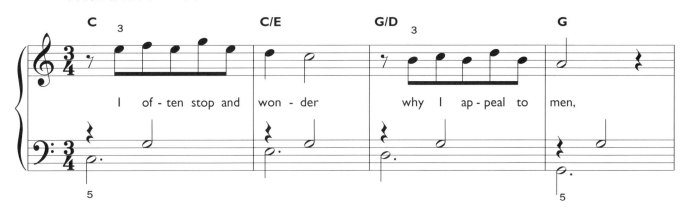

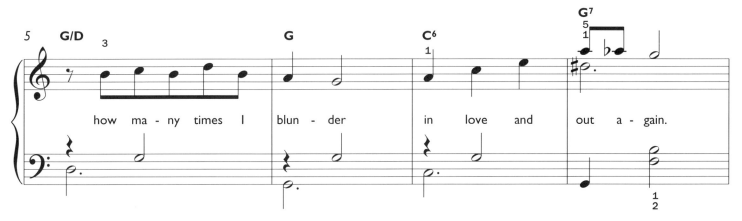

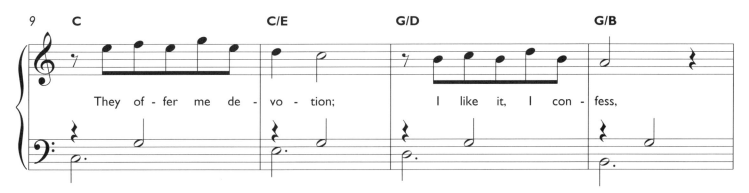

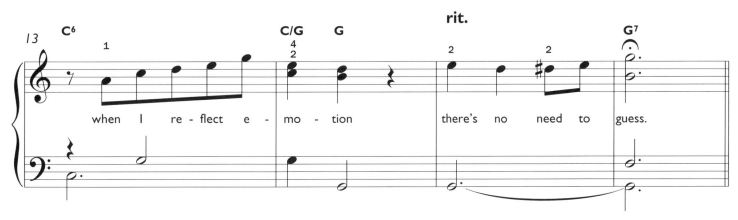

A tempo

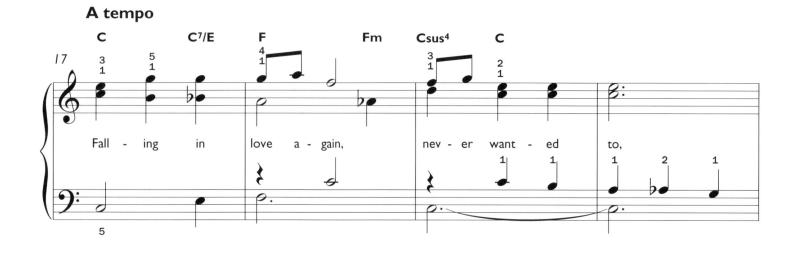

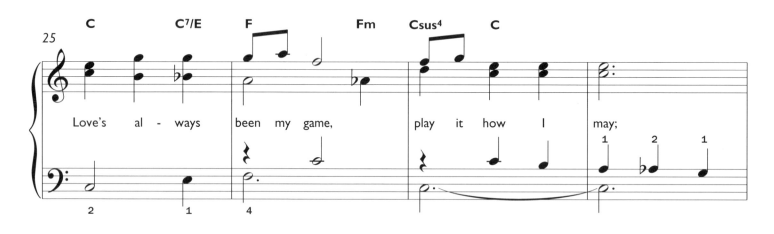

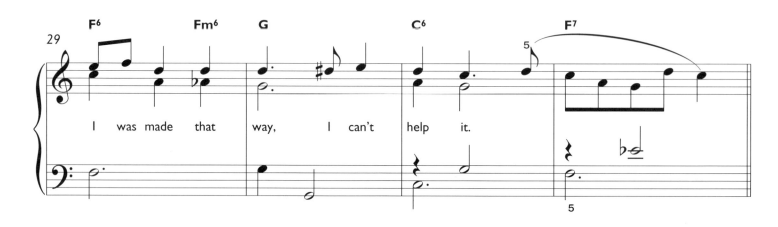

12

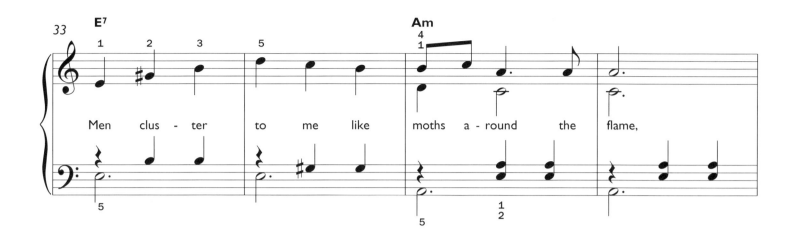

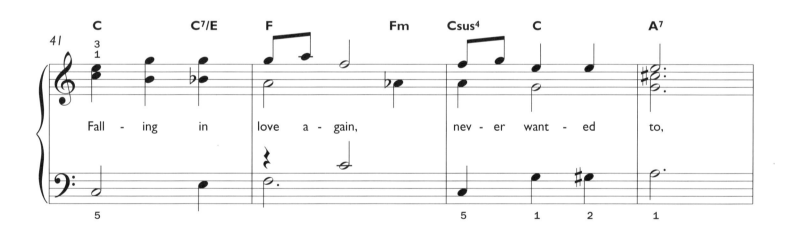

IF MY FRIENDS COULD SEE ME NOW

Words by Dorothy Fields
Music by Cy Coleman

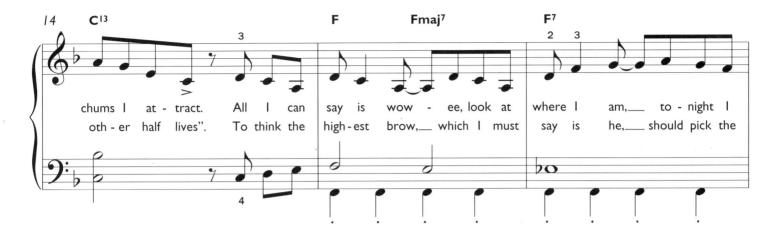

to Coda ⊕

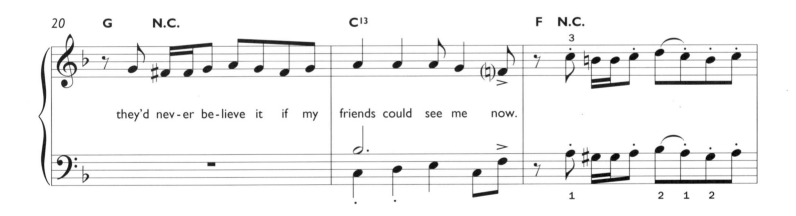

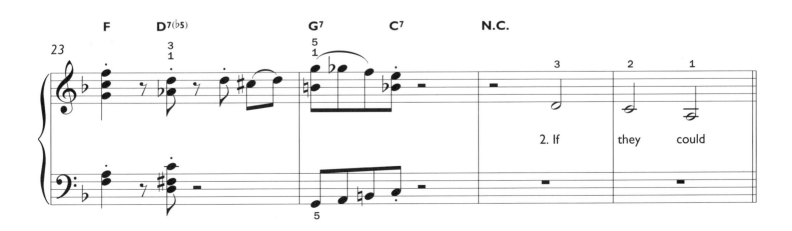

I AM A VAMP

Words by Marcellus Schiffer

Music by Mischa Spolinsky

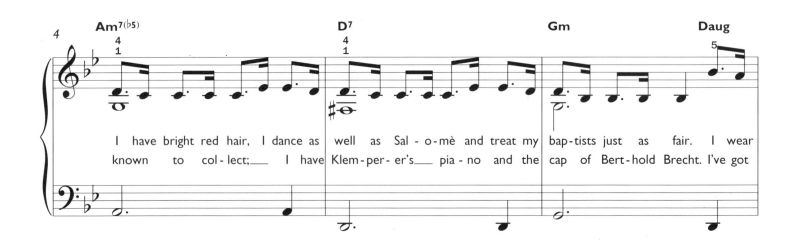

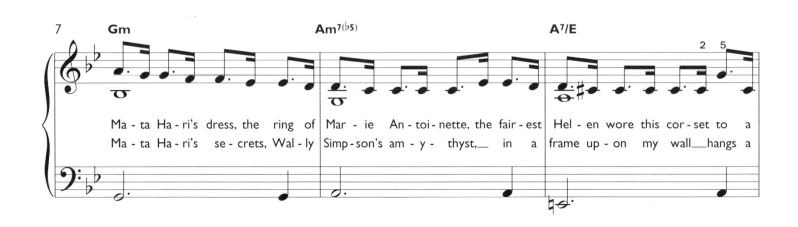

18

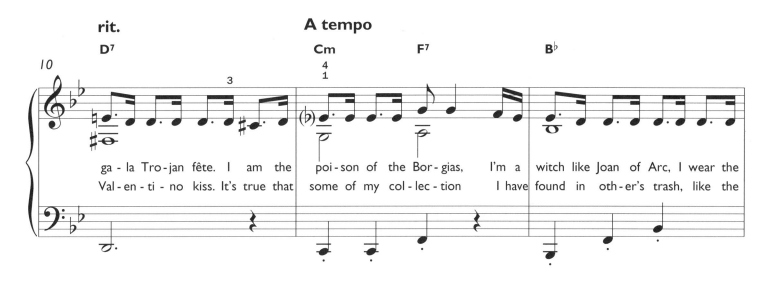

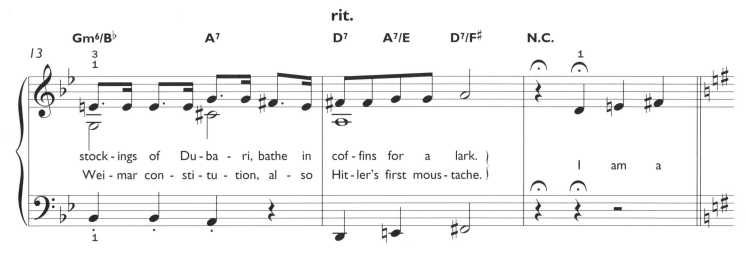

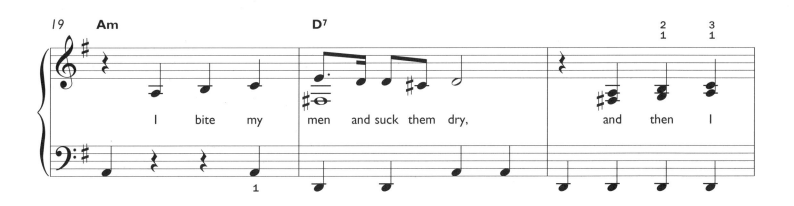

bake them in a pie.   I am a   vamp,   I am a

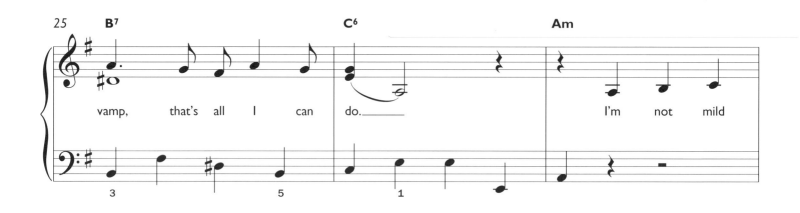

vamp,   that's all I can   do._____   I'm not mild

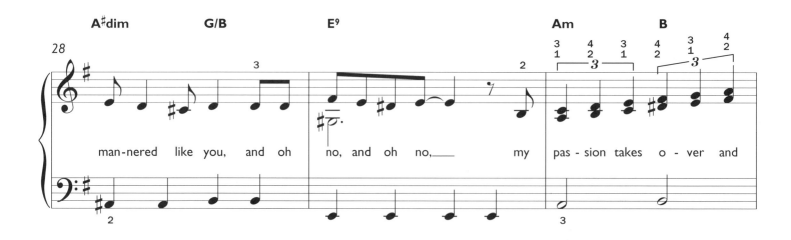

man-nered like you,   and oh   no, and oh no,___   my   pas - sion takes o - ver and

off   I go! I should real - ly be kept___ in a   zoo.   zoo.

The Ladies Who Lunch

Words & Music by Stephen Sondheim

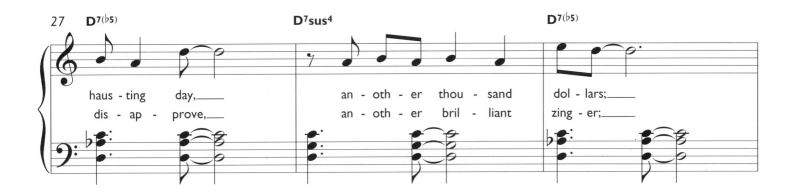

haus - ting day,_____ an - oth - er thou - sand dol - lars;_____
dis - ap - prove,_____ an - oth - er bril - liant zing - er;

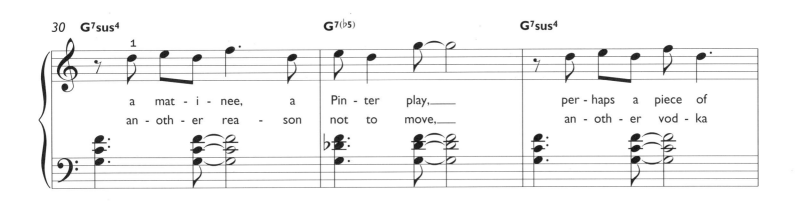

a mat - i - nee, a Pin - ter play,_____ per - haps a piece of
an - oth - er rea - son not to move,_____ an - oth - er vod - ka

Mah - ler's;_____ I'll drink to that!
sting - er;_____ I'll drink to that!

(Spoken) ...And one for Mahler!

3. Here's to the girls who play wife,_____
5. So here's to the girls on the go,_____

23

24

D.S. al Coda

$\oplus$ **Coda**

MAKIN' WHOOPEE

Words by Gus Kahn
Music by Walter Donaldson

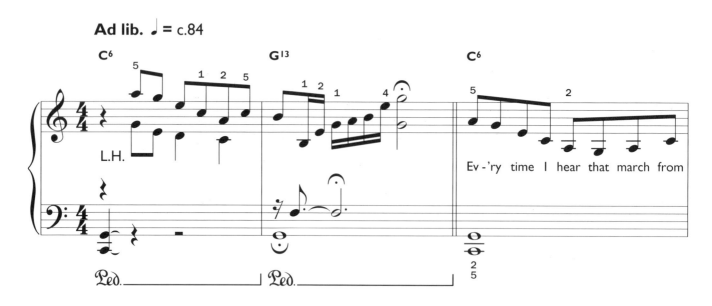

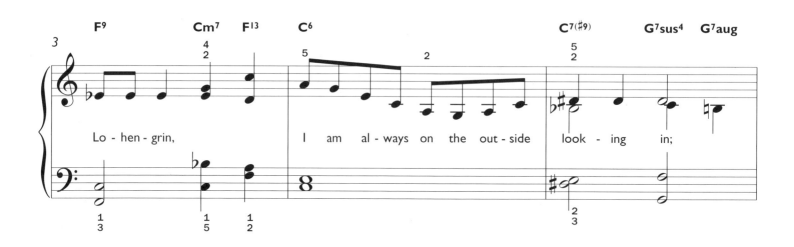

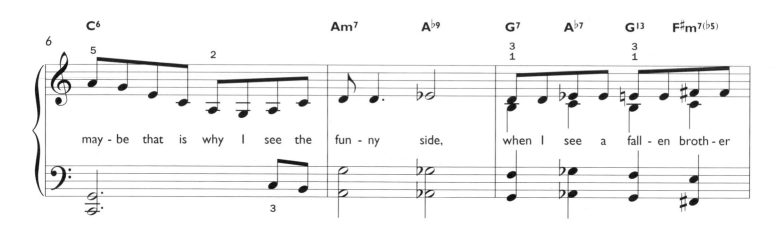

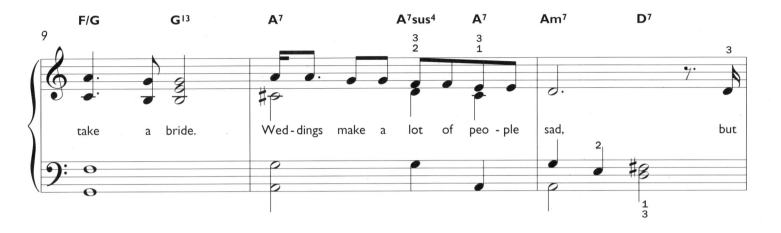

take a bride. Wed-dings make a lot of peo-ple sad, but

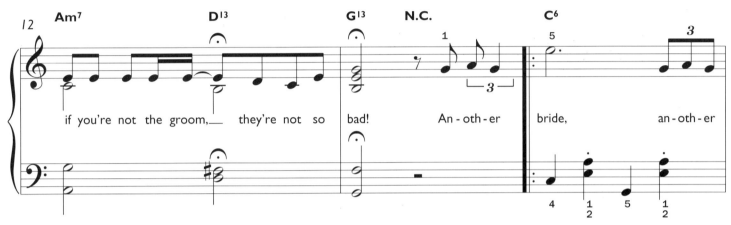

if you're not the groom,___ they're not so bad! An-oth-er bride, an-oth-er

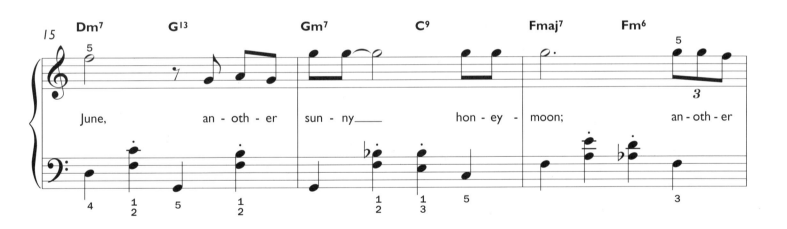

June, an-oth-er sun-ny___ hon-ey - moon; an-oth-er

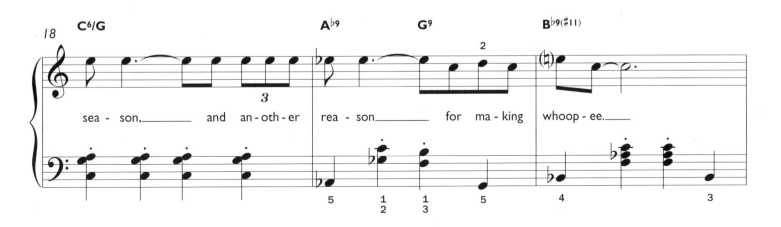

sea - son,___ and an-oth-er rea-son___ for ma-king whoop-ee.___

27

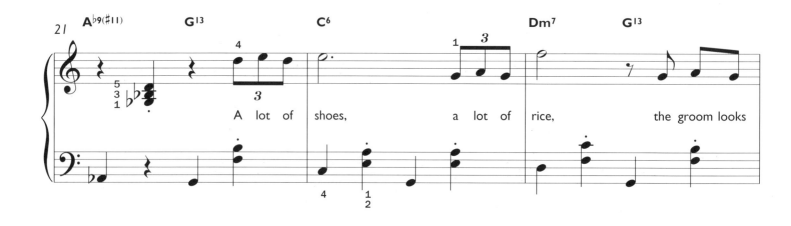

A lot of shoes, a lot of rice, the groom looks

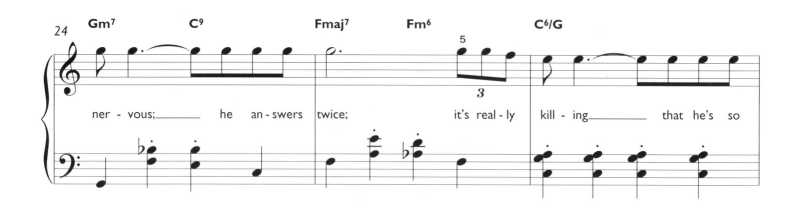

ner - vous; he an - swers twice; it's real - ly kill - ing that he's so

will - ing to make whoop- ee.

Pic - ture a lit - tle love nest, down where the ro - ses

cling; pic-ture that same___ sweet love nest,___ think what a year___ can

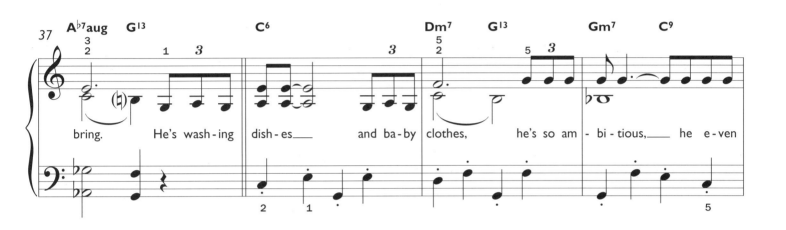

bring. He's wash-ing dish-es___ and ba-by clothes, he's so am - bi-tious,___ he e-ven

sews; but don't for-get folks,___ that's___ what you get folks___ for ma-king

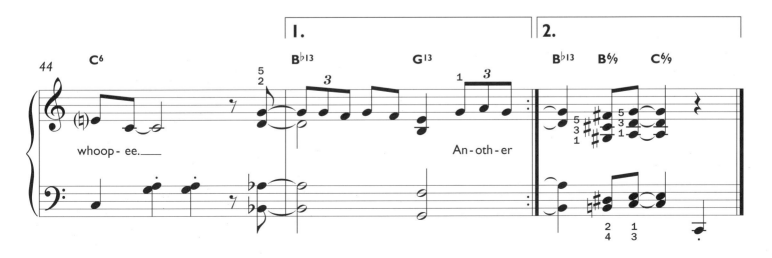

whoop-ee.___   An-oth-er

THE MAN THAT GOT AWAY

Words by Ira Gershwin
Music by Harold Arlen

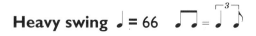

Heavy swing ♩ = 66

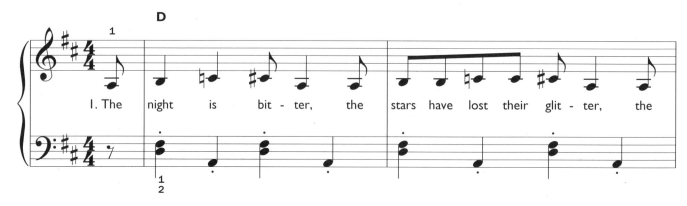

1. The night is bit-ter, the stars have lost their glit-ter, the

winds grow cold-er, sud-den-ly you're old-er; and all be-cause___ of the

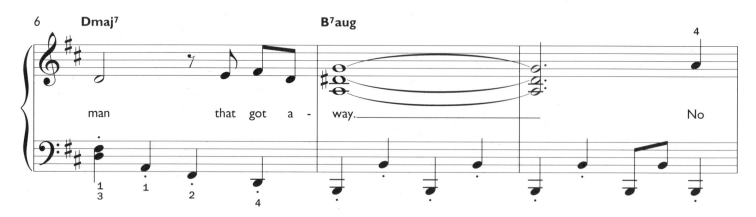

man that got a - way.___ No

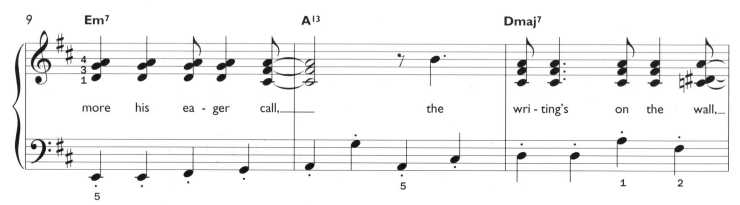

more his ea-ger call,___ the wri-ting's on the wall,___

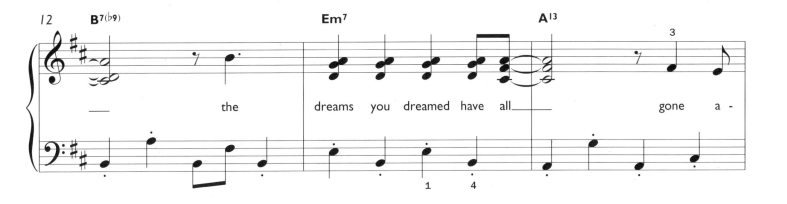

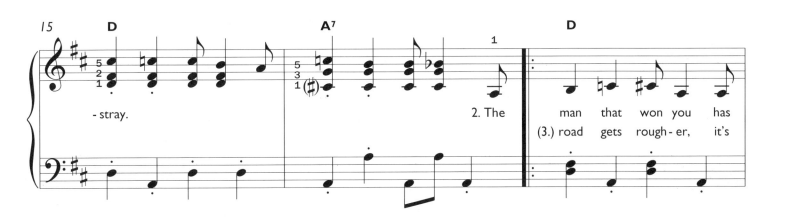

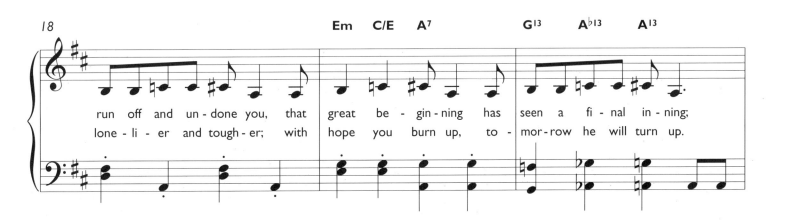

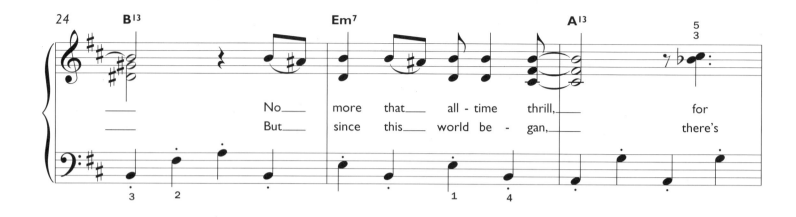

No⎯ more that⎯ all-time thrill,⎯ for
But⎯ since this⎯ world be - gan,⎯ there's

1.

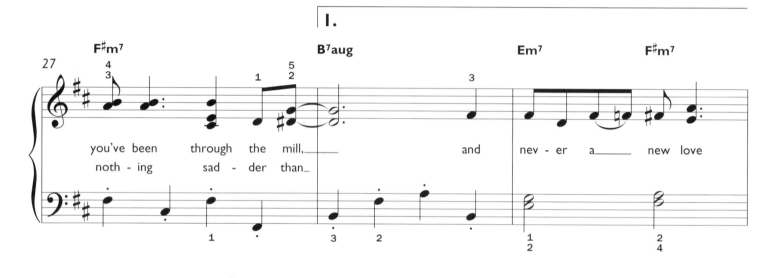

you've been through the mill,⎯ and nev-er a⎯ new love
noth - ing sad - der than⎯

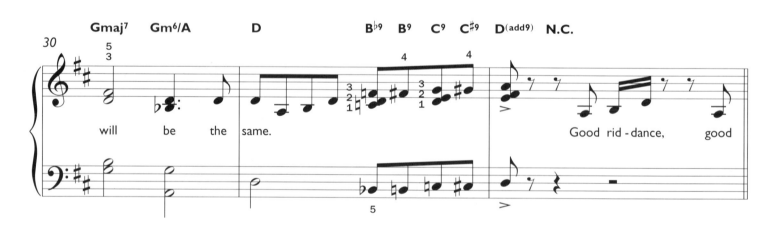

will be the same. Good rid-dance, good

- bye, ev-'ry trick of his⎯ you're on

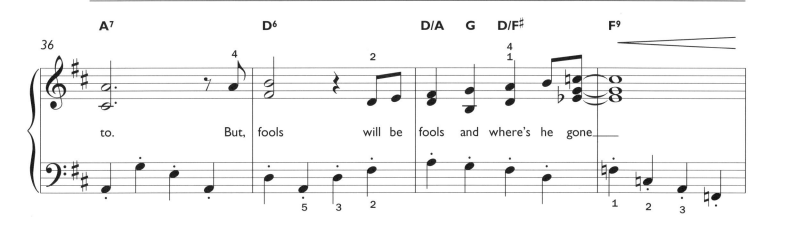

to. But, fools will be fools and where's he gone

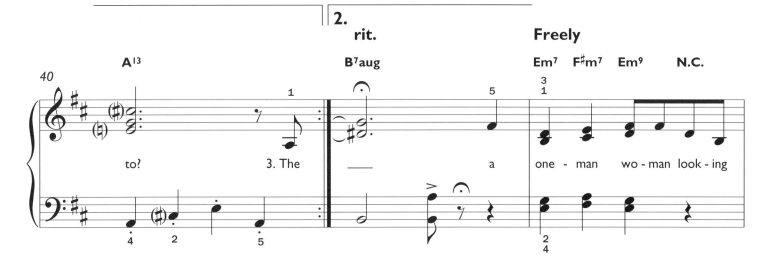

to? 3. The a one-man wo-man look-ing

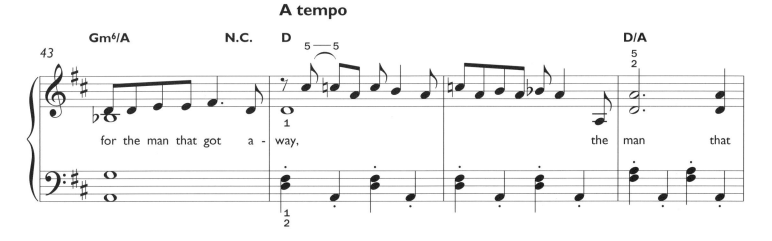

for the man that got a-way, the man that

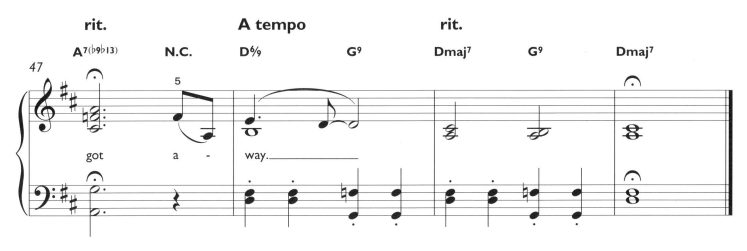

got a-way.

MAYBE THIS TIME

Words by Fred Ebb
Music by John Kander

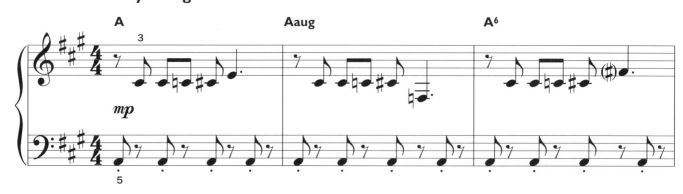

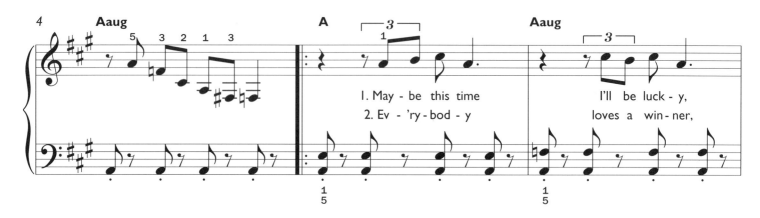

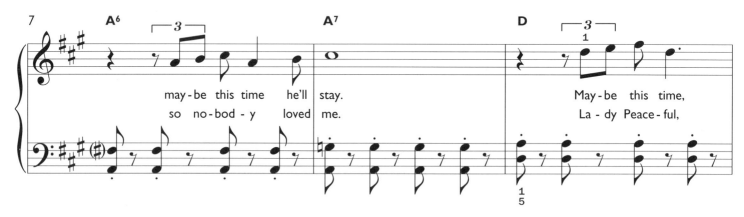

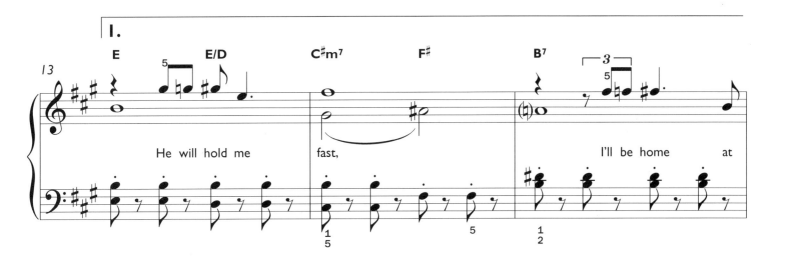

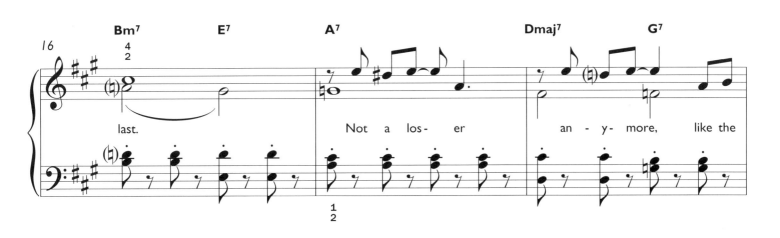

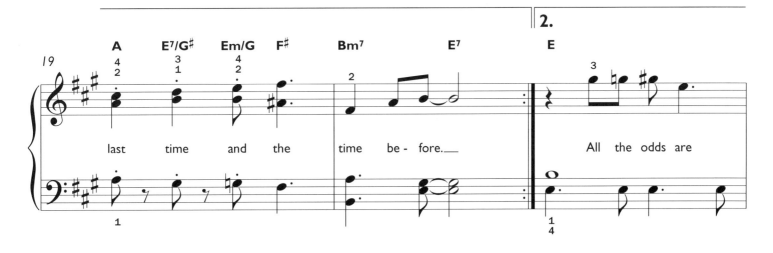

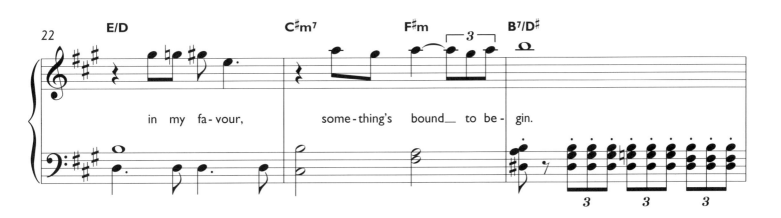

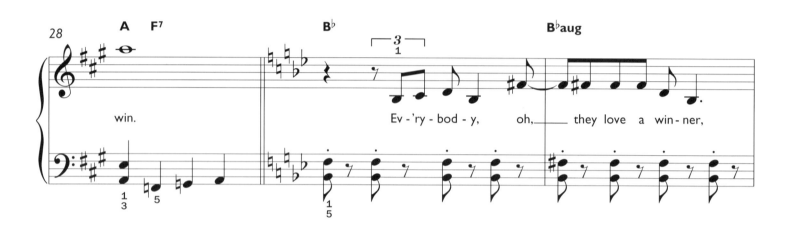

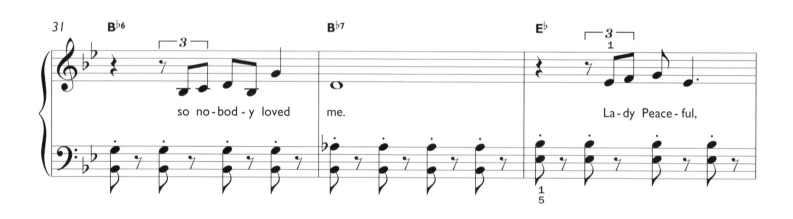

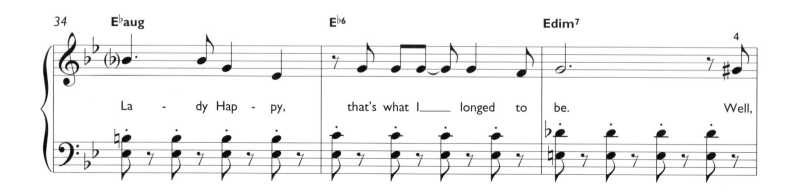

all   the odds are   there in my fa - vour,   some - thing's bound___ to be -

- gin.   It's got - ta hap - pen,   hap - pen some - time,

rit.   **A tempo**

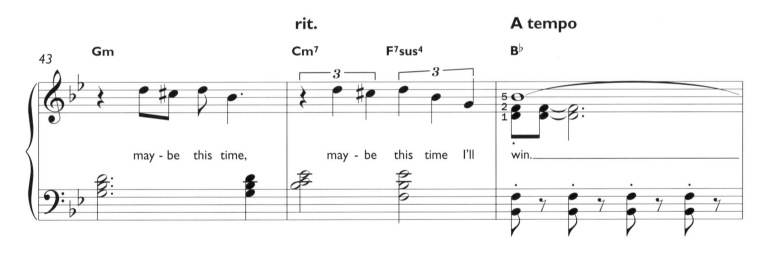

may - be this time,   may - be this time I'll   win.___

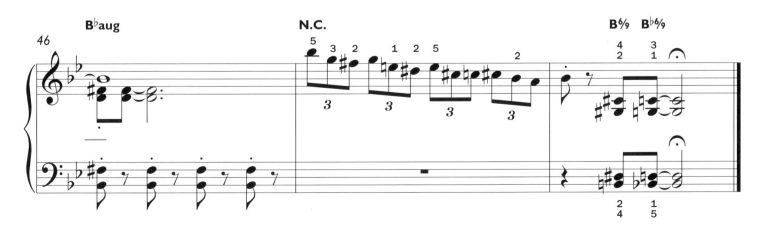

LET ME ENTERTAIN YOU

Words by Stephen Sondheim
Music by Jule Styne

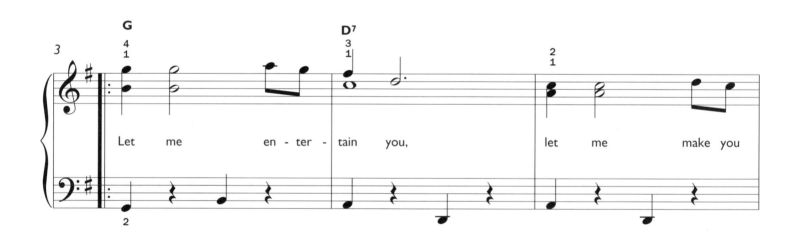

Let me en - ter - tain you, let me make you

smile.

Let me do a few tricks, some

old and then some new tricks, I'm ve - ry ver - sa - tile.

And if you're real good, I'll make you feel good;

I want your spi - rits to climb. So let me en - ter-

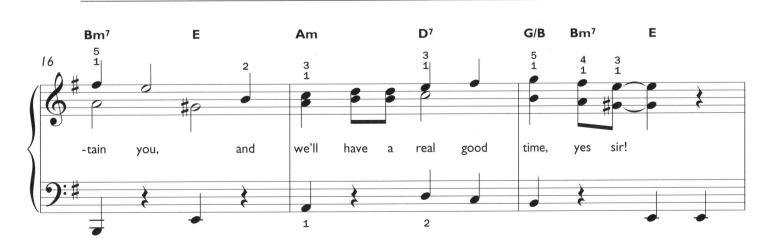

-tain you, and we'll have a real good time, yes sir!

We'll have___ a real good time.

2.

Let me en - ter - tain you, and

we'll have a real good time.___

rit.

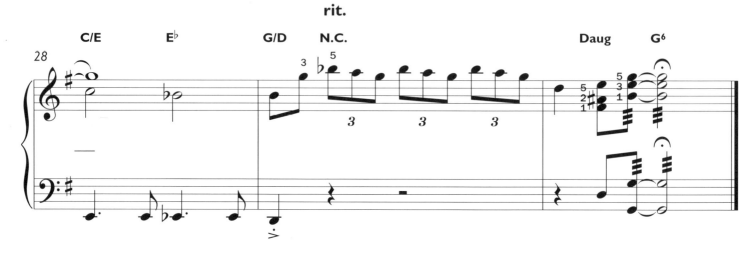

MEIN HERR

Words by Fred Ebb
Music by John Kander

lie - ber Herr,__ fare - well, mein lie - ber Herr,__ it was a fine af - fair,___ but now it's

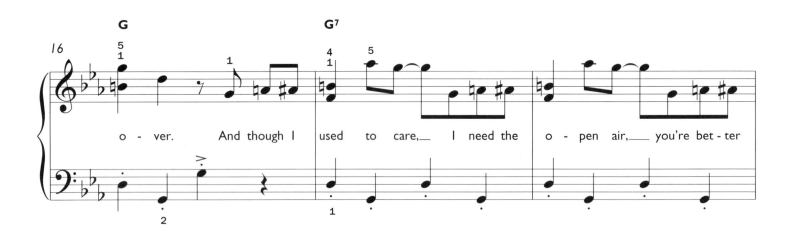

o - ver. And though I used to care,__ I need the o - pen air,___ you're bet - ter

♩ = 120

off with - out__ me, mein Herr. Don't dab your eye, mein Herr,__ or won - der

why, mein Herr,__ I've al - ways said that I__ was a ro - ver. You must - n't

knit your brow,__ you should have known by now__ you'd ev -'ry cause to doubt__ me, mein

1.
Herr.   2. The

2.
Herr.   Bye bye, mein

lie - ber Herr,____ auf wie - der - sehen, mein Herr,____ es war sehr

gut, mein Herr__ and vor - bei.____ Du kennst mich wohl, mein Herr,__ ach le - be

wohl, mein Herr,____ du sollst mich nicht mehr se - hen, mein Herr.

TAKE ME TO YOUR HEART AGAIN
(LA VIE EN ROSE)

Words by Edith Piaf
Music by R.S. Louiguy

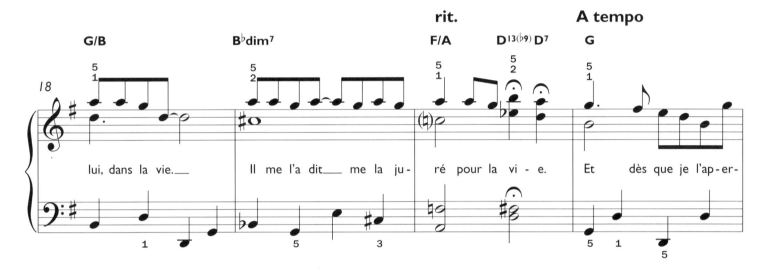

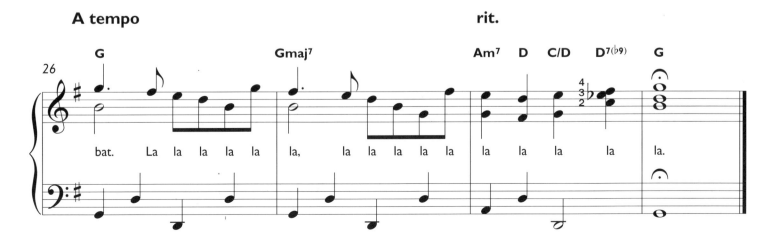

NO REGRETS
(NON, JE NE REGRETTE RIEN)

Words by Michel Vaucaire
Music by Charles Dumont

March-like ♩. = 92

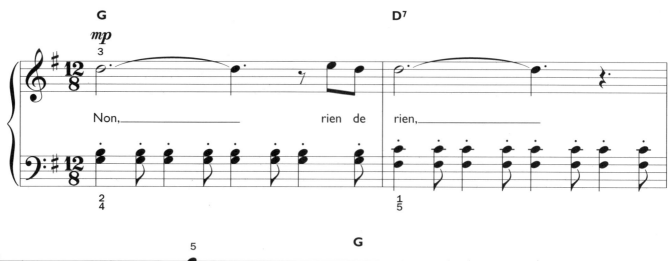

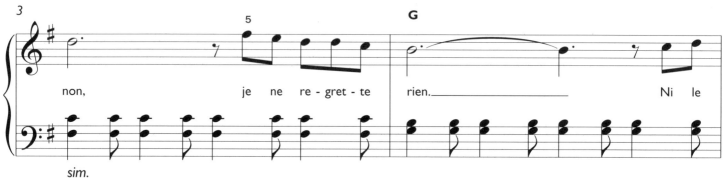

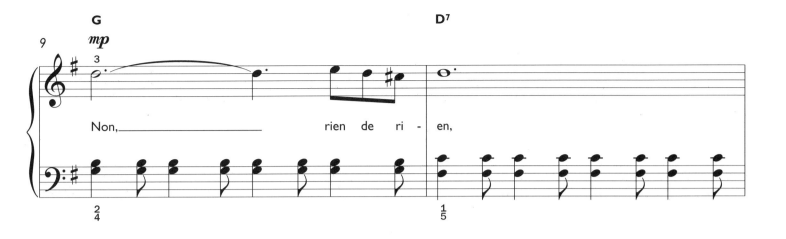

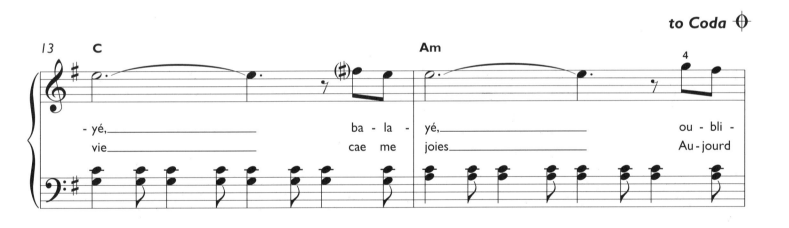